LITTLE BLUE TRUCK COLORING BOOK

Little Blue

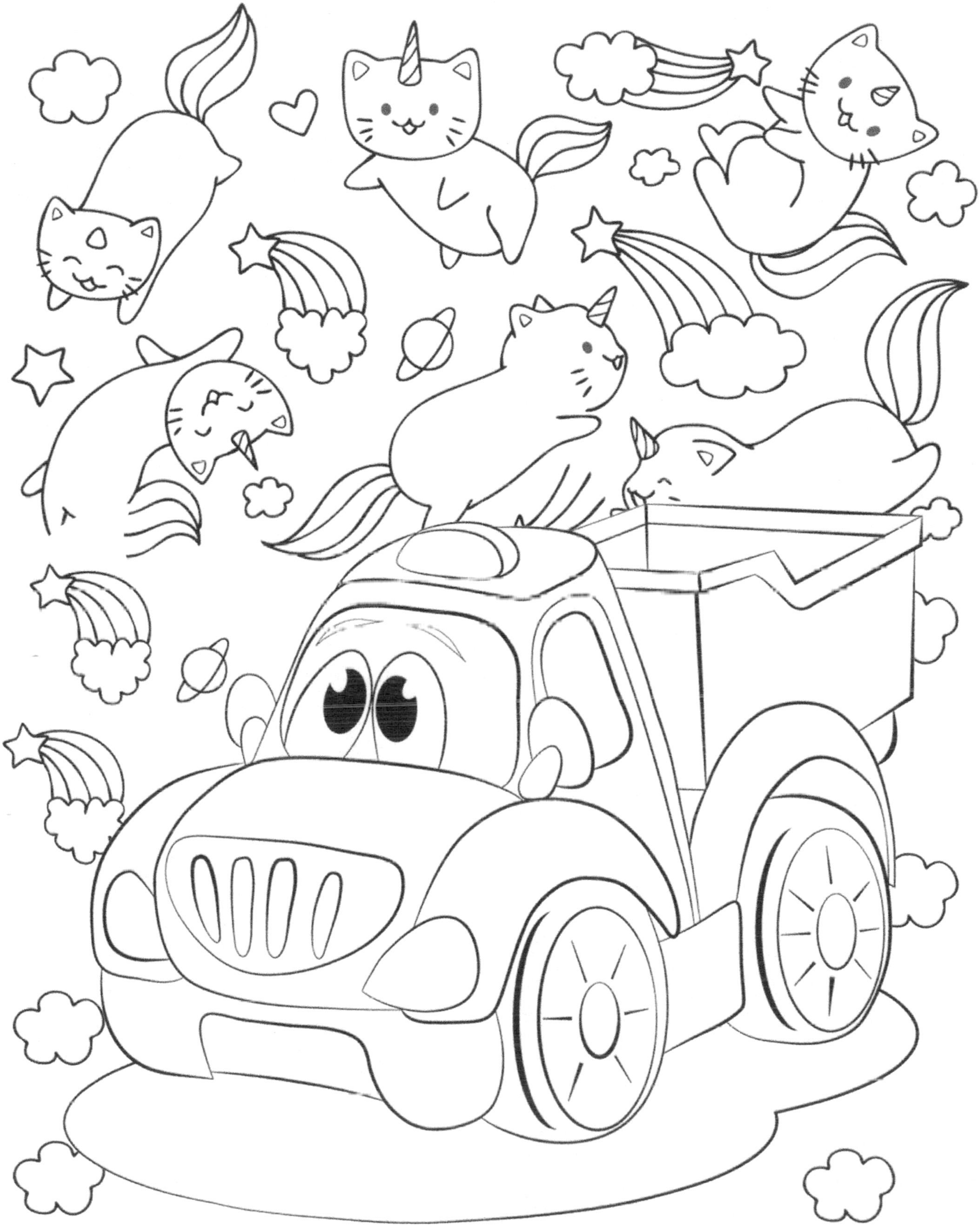

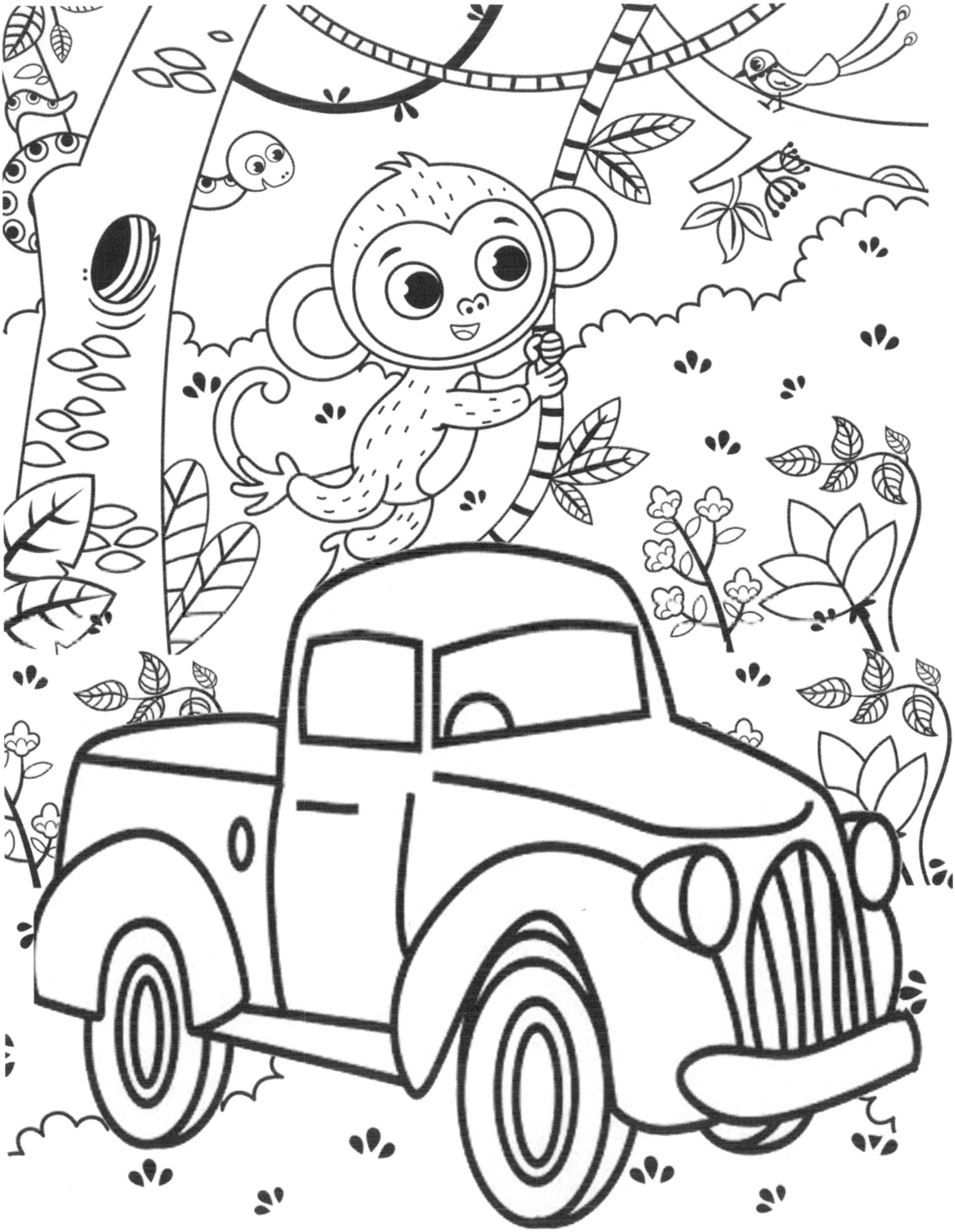

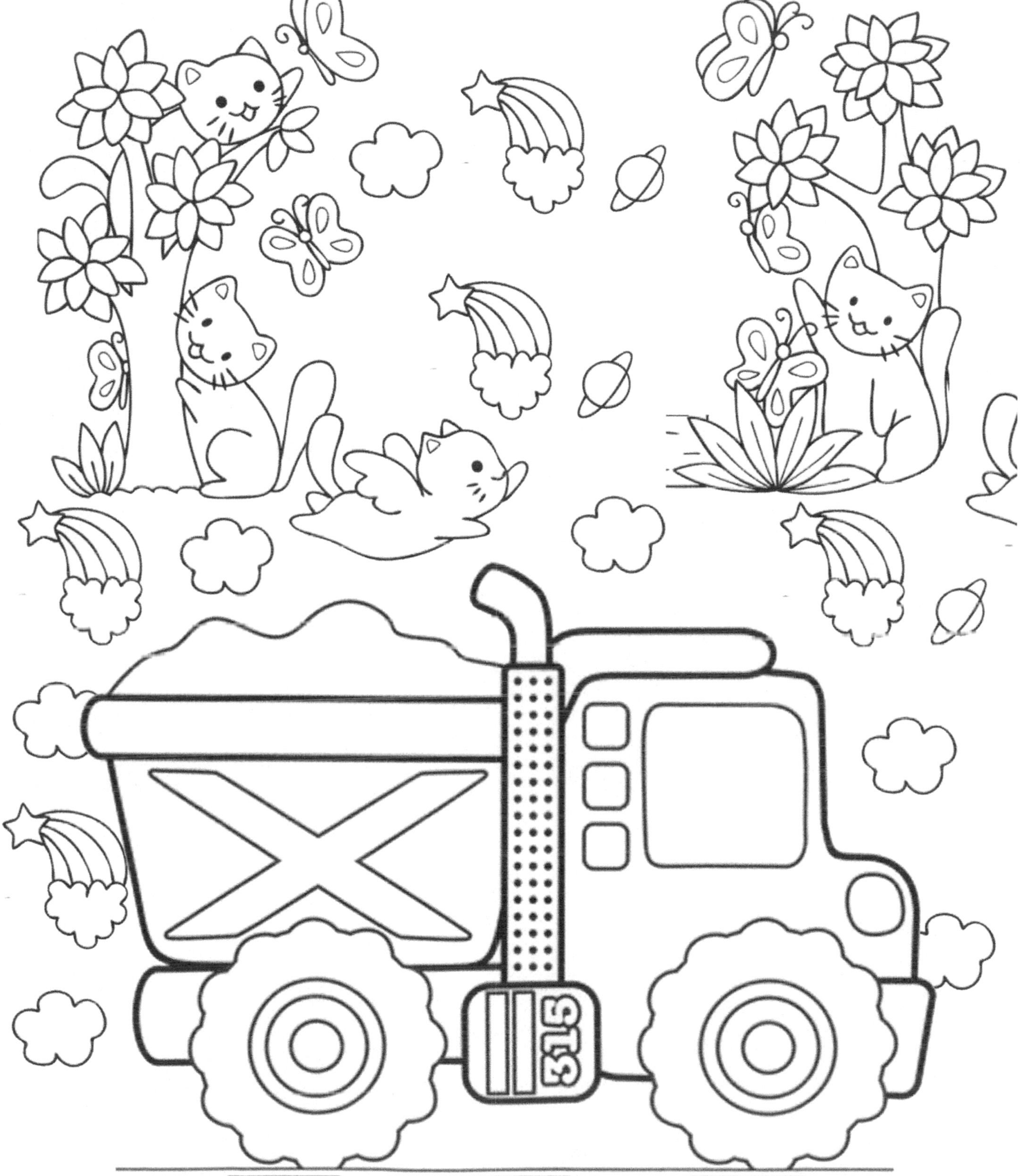

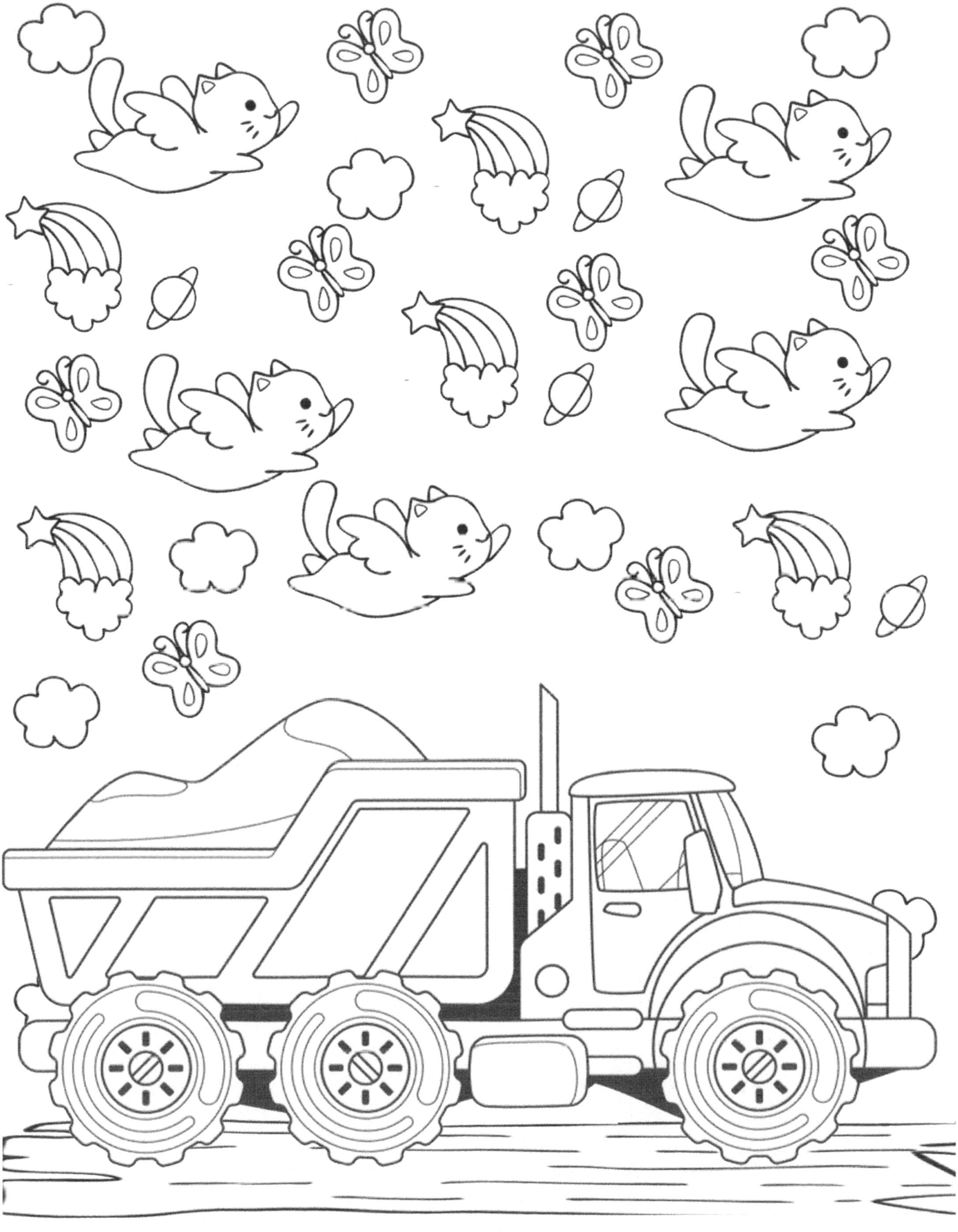

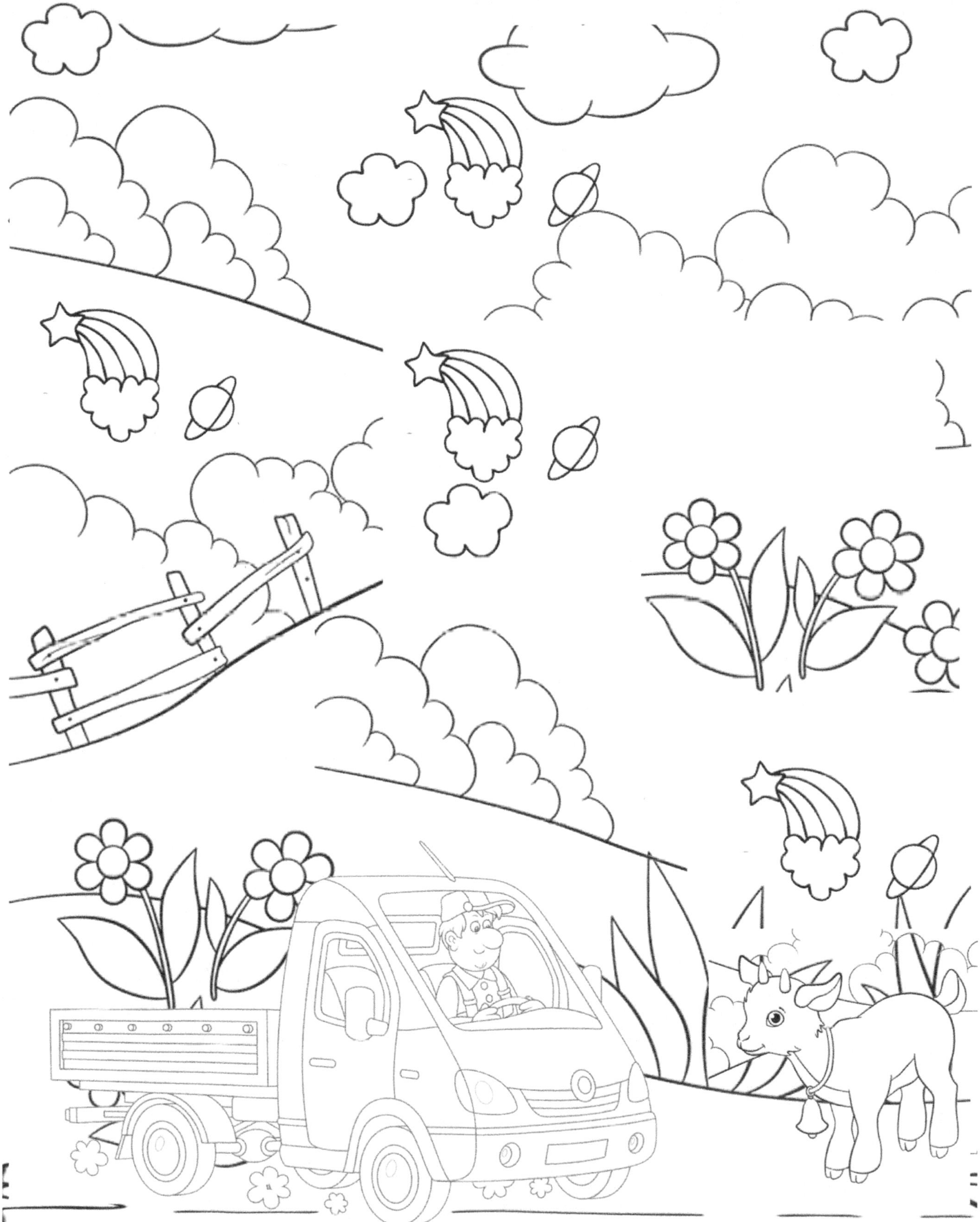

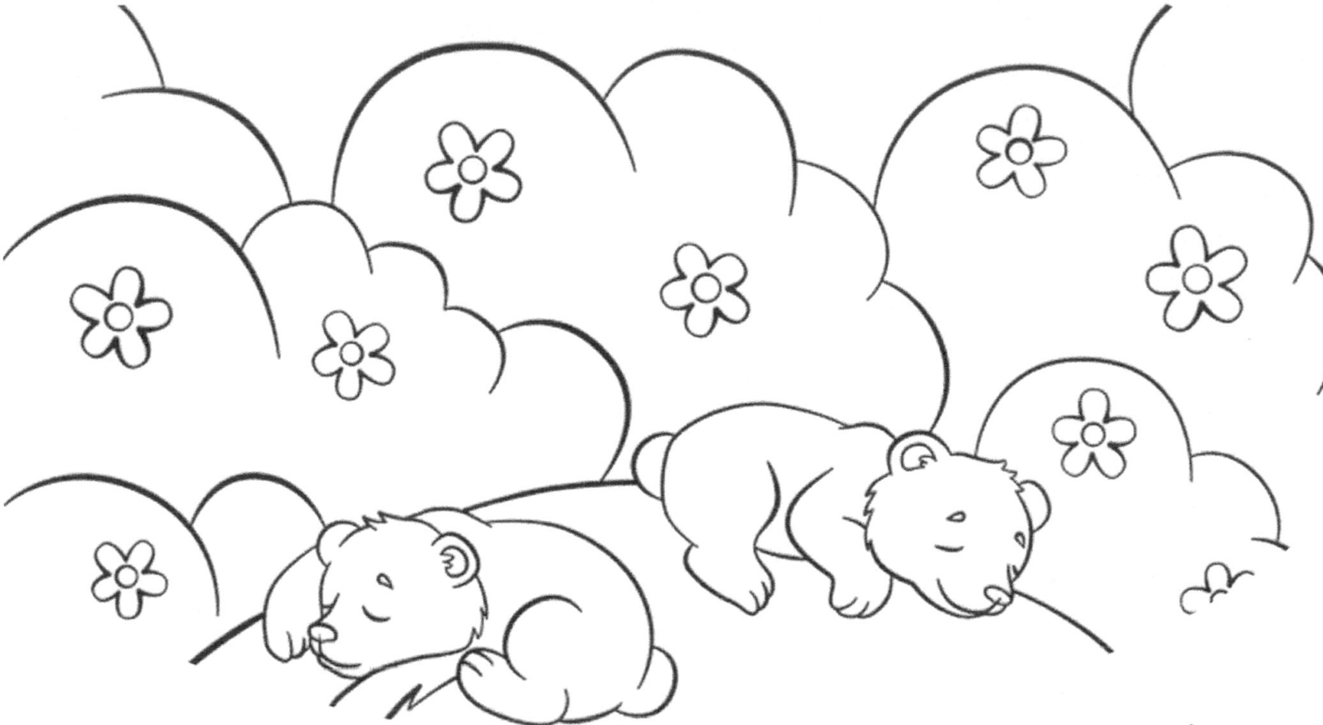

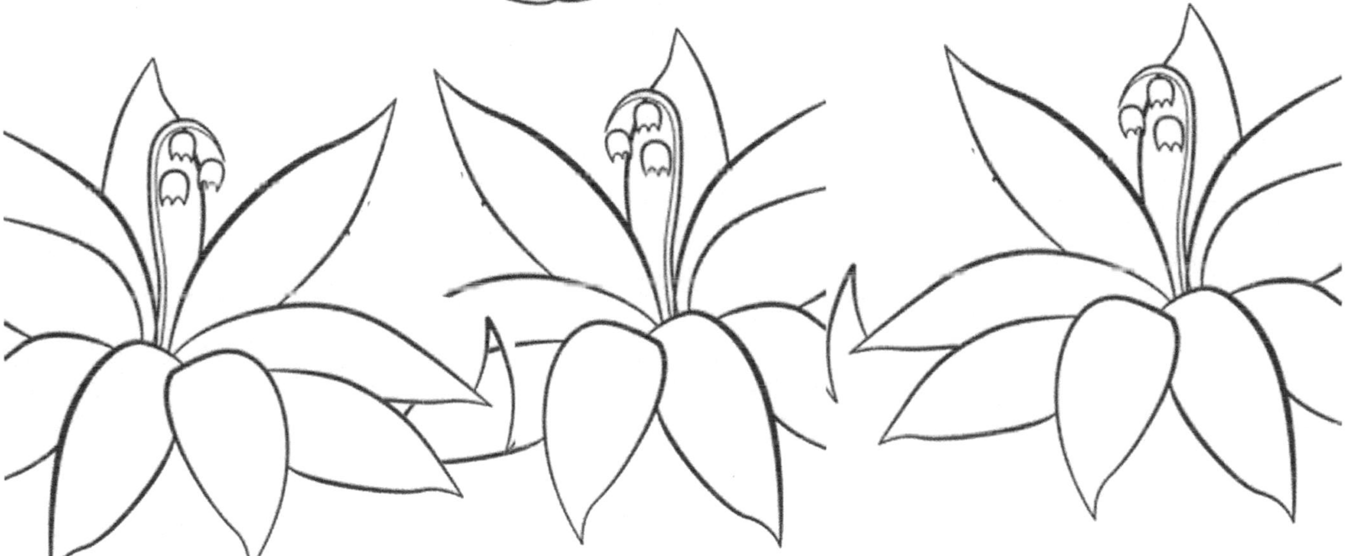

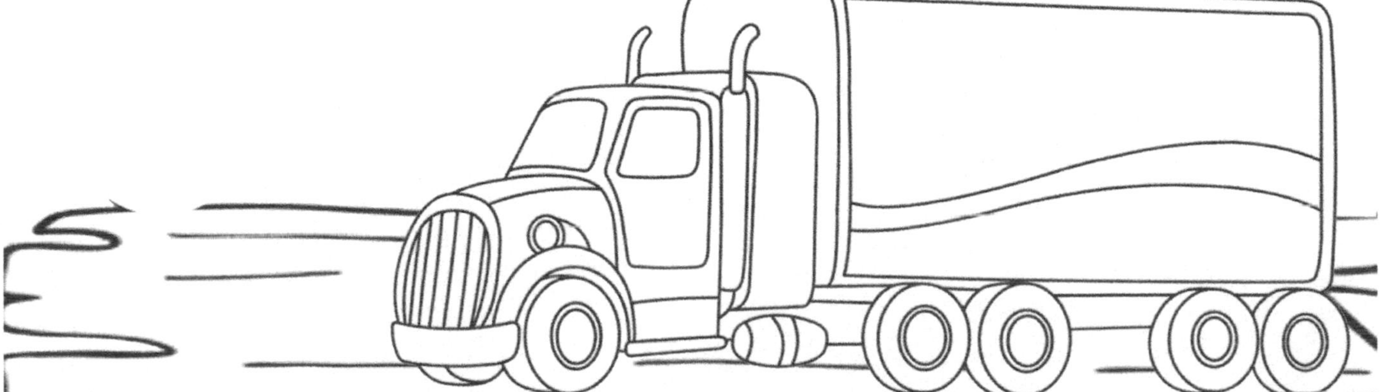

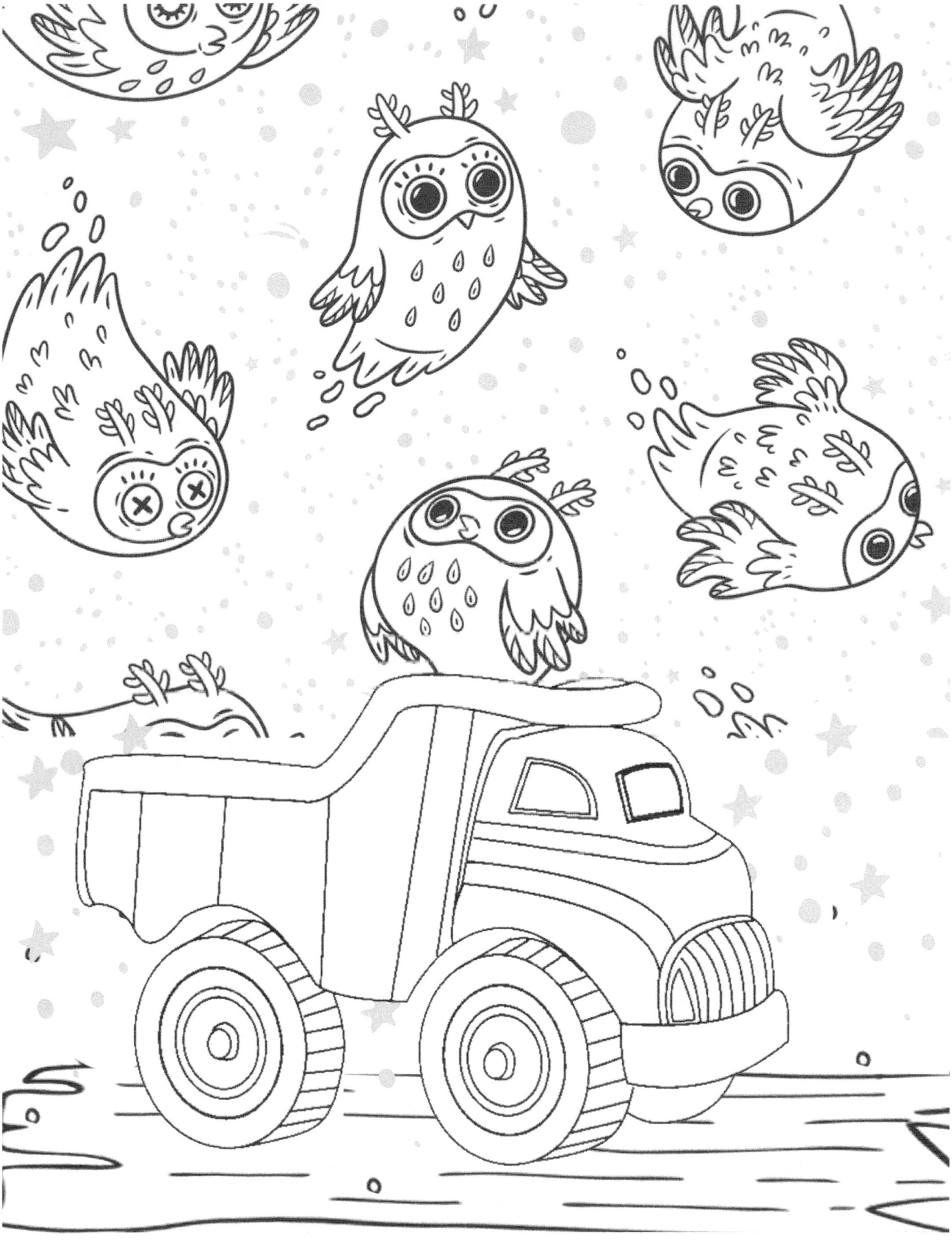

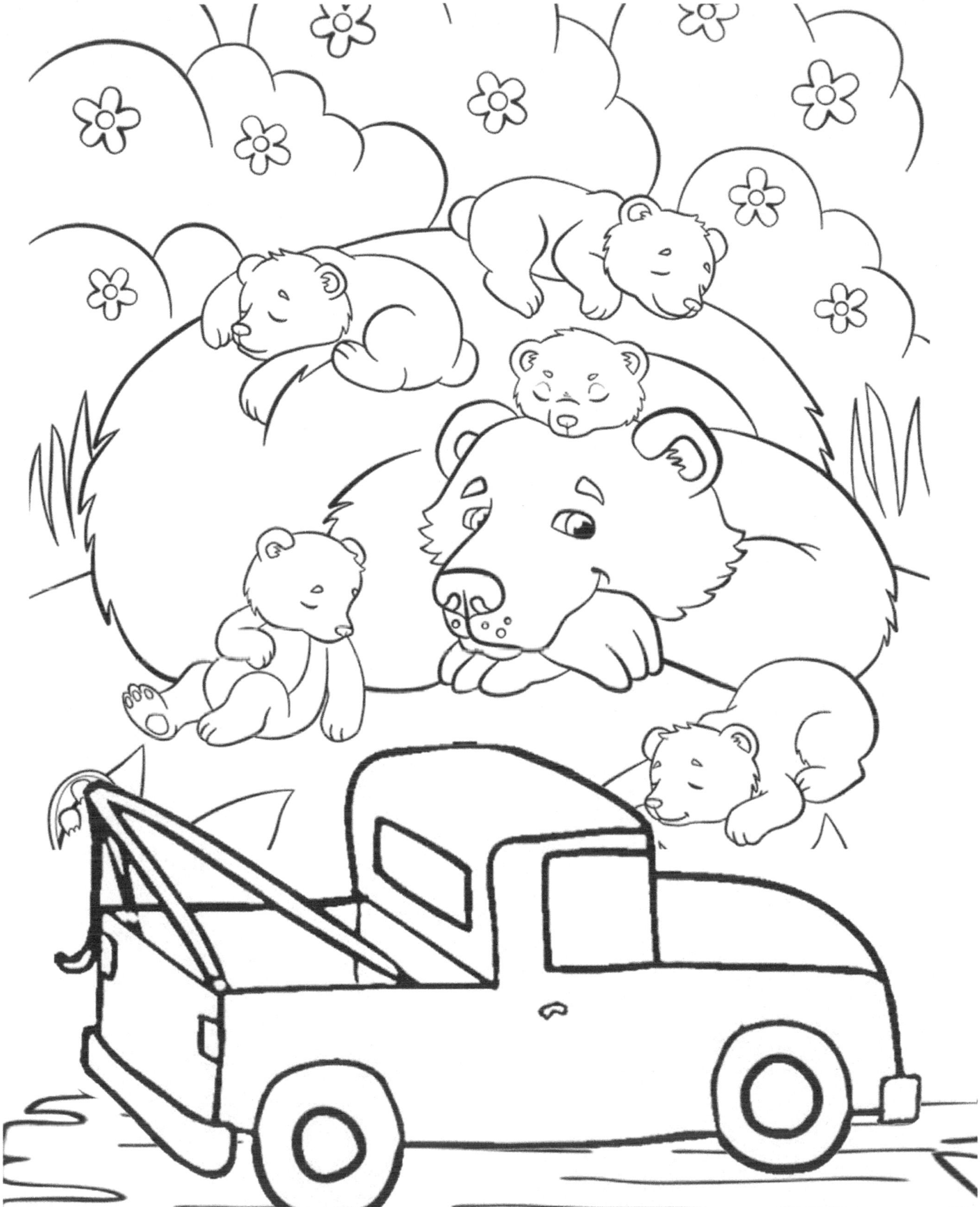

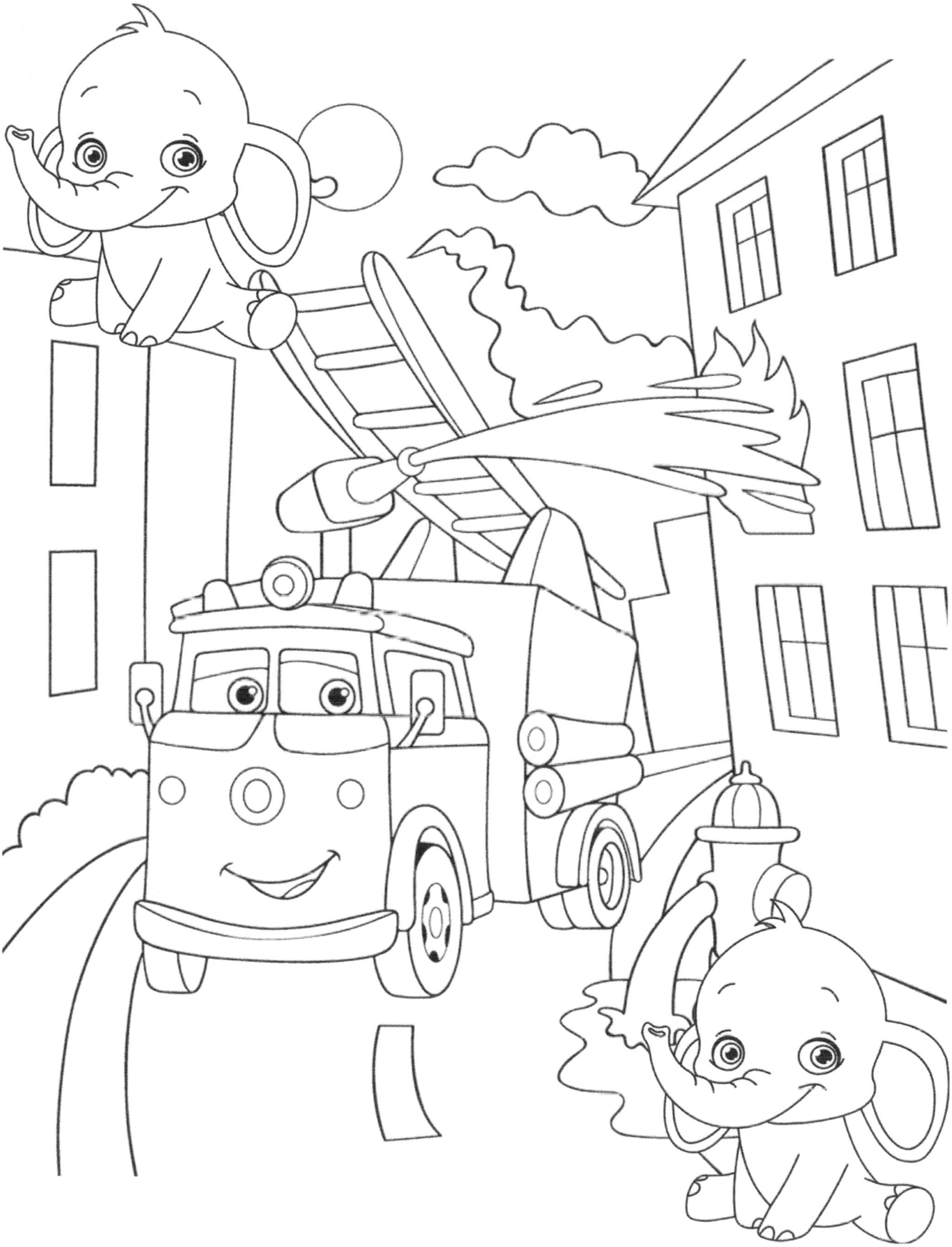

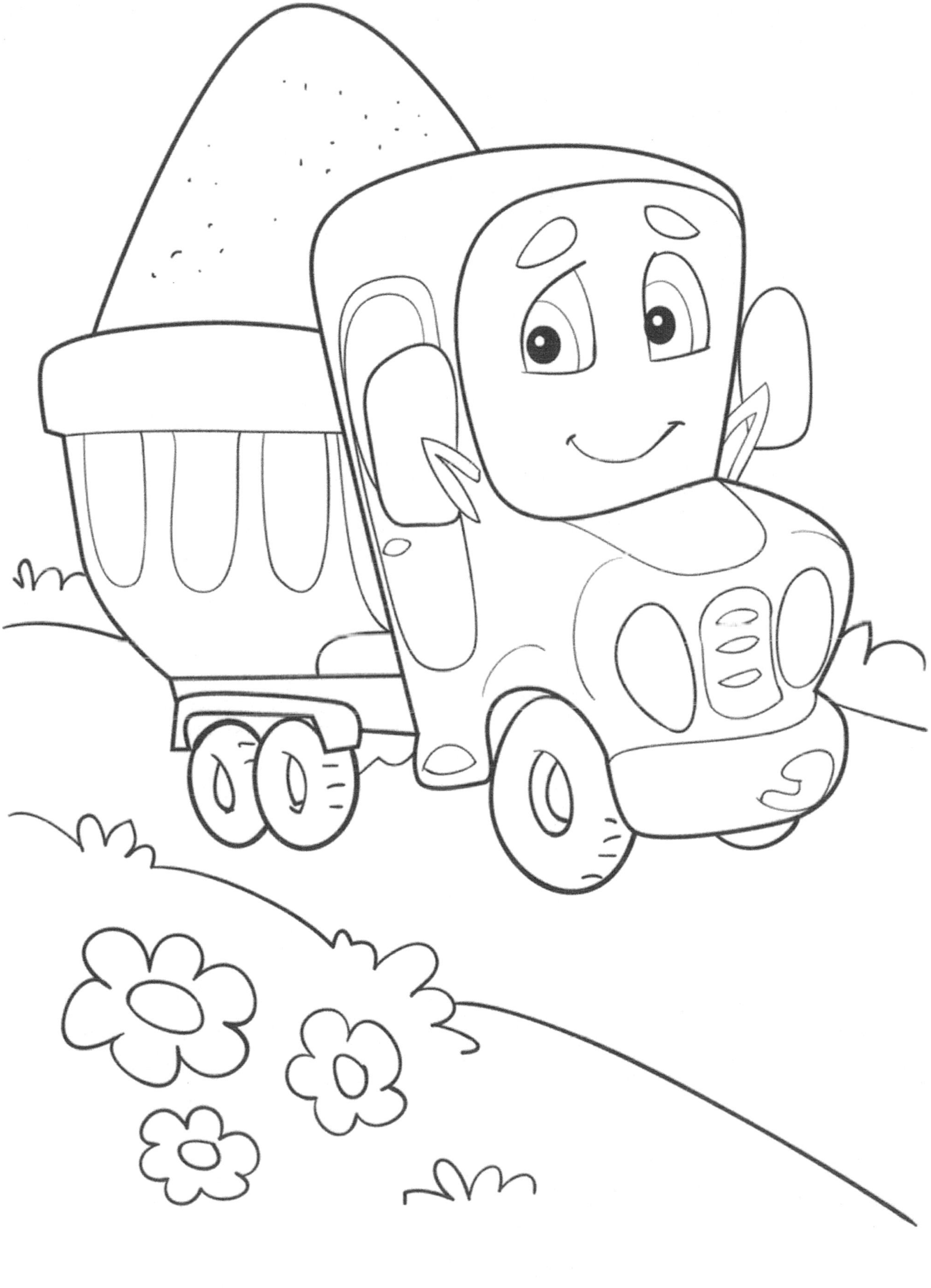

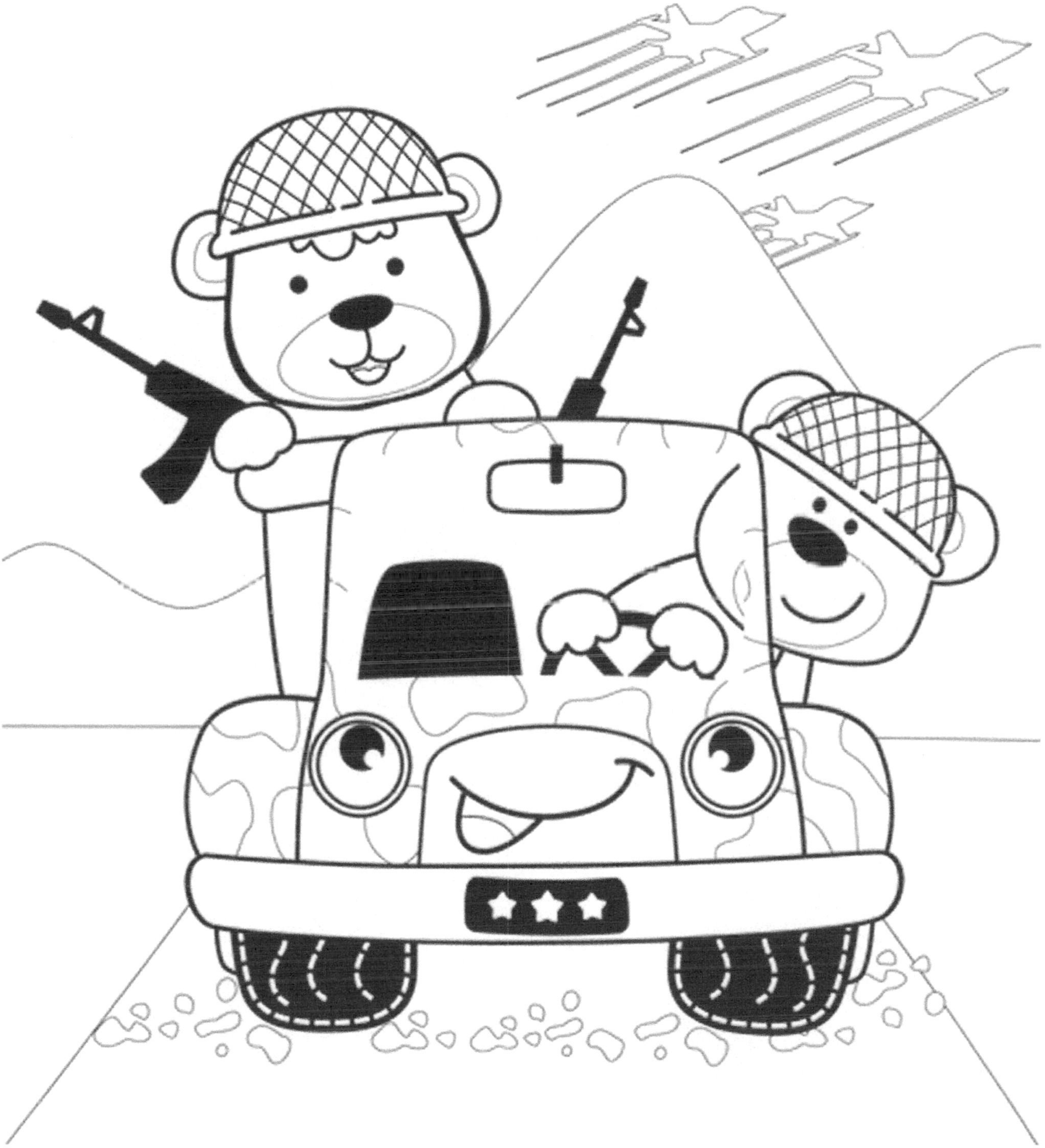

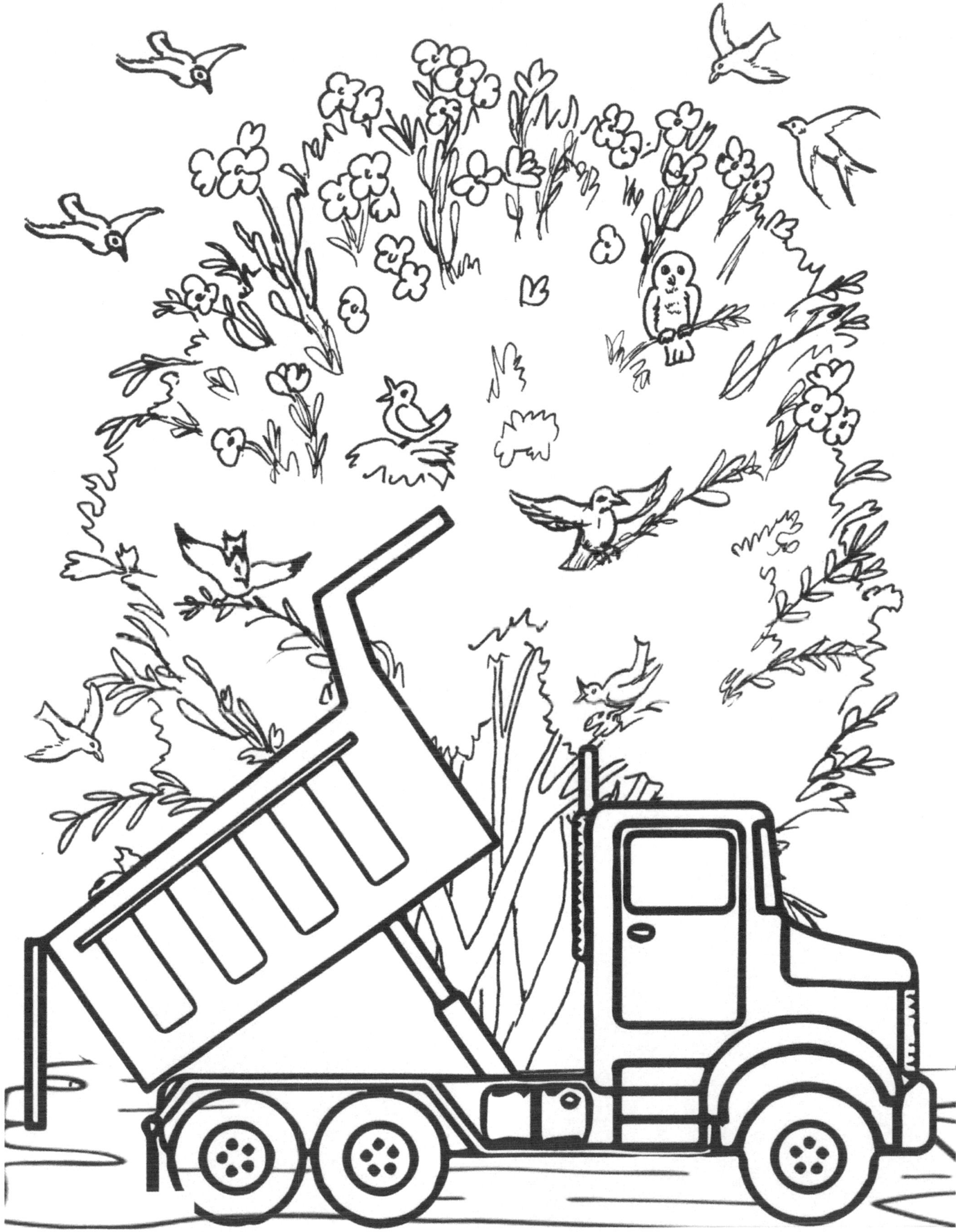

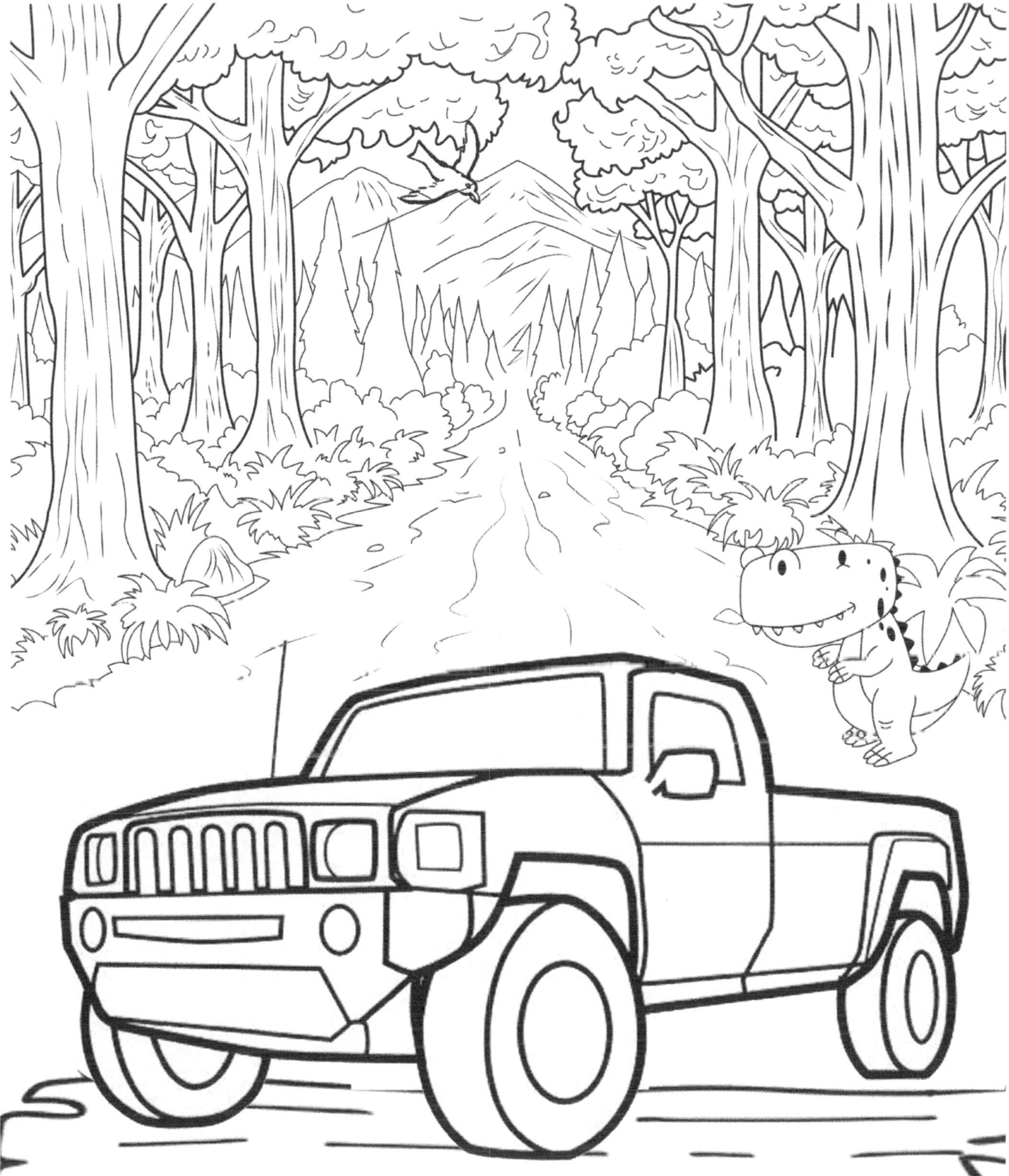

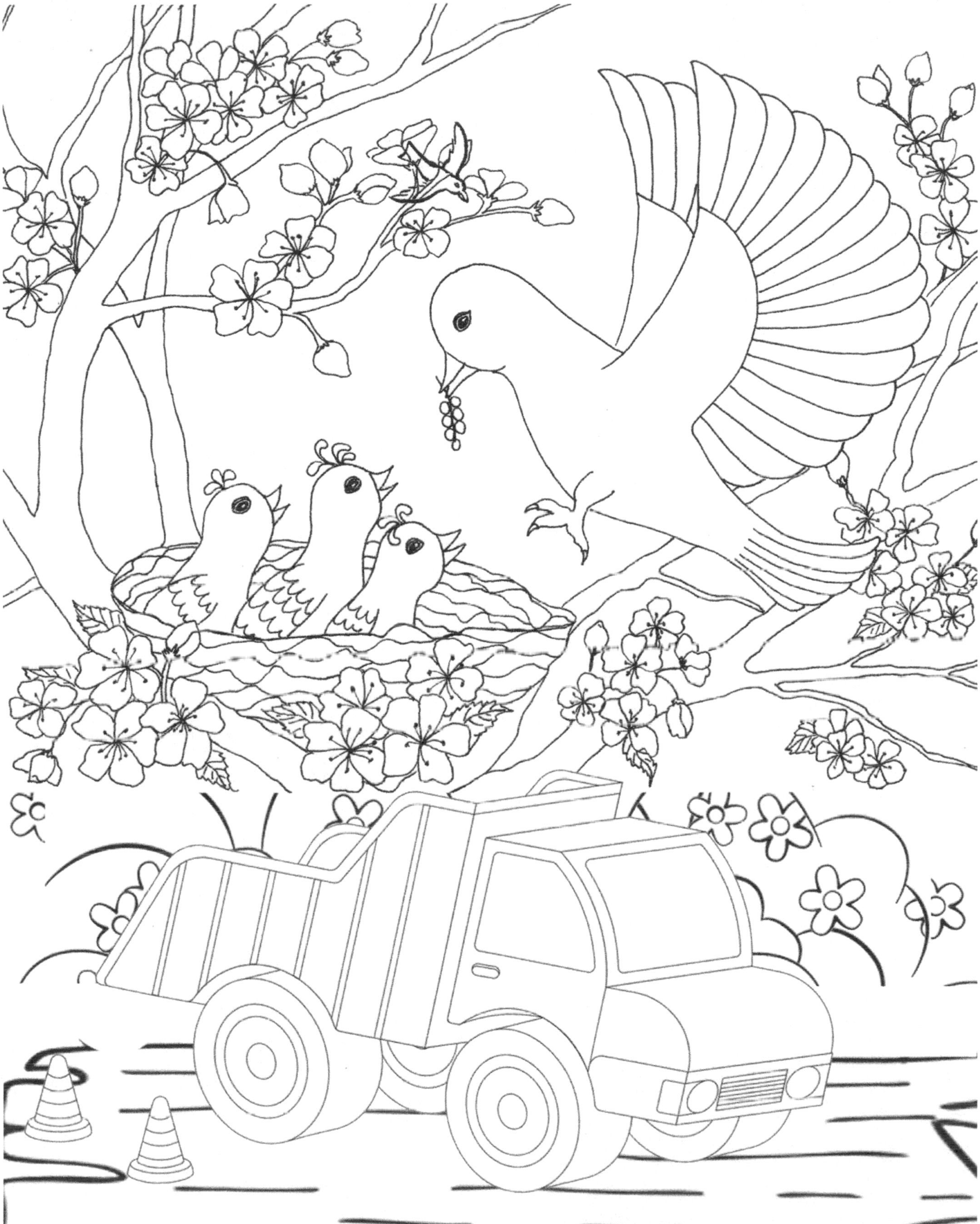

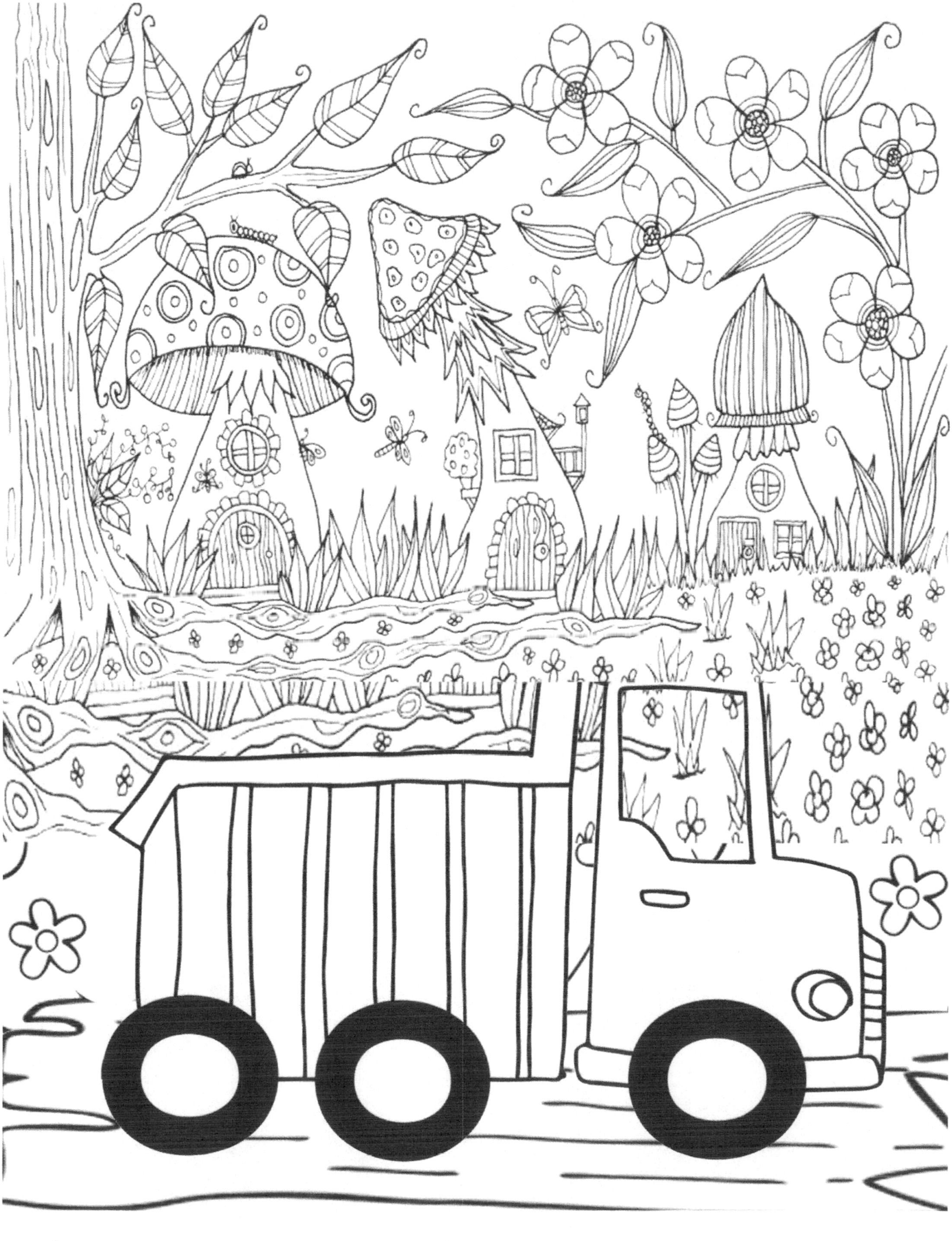

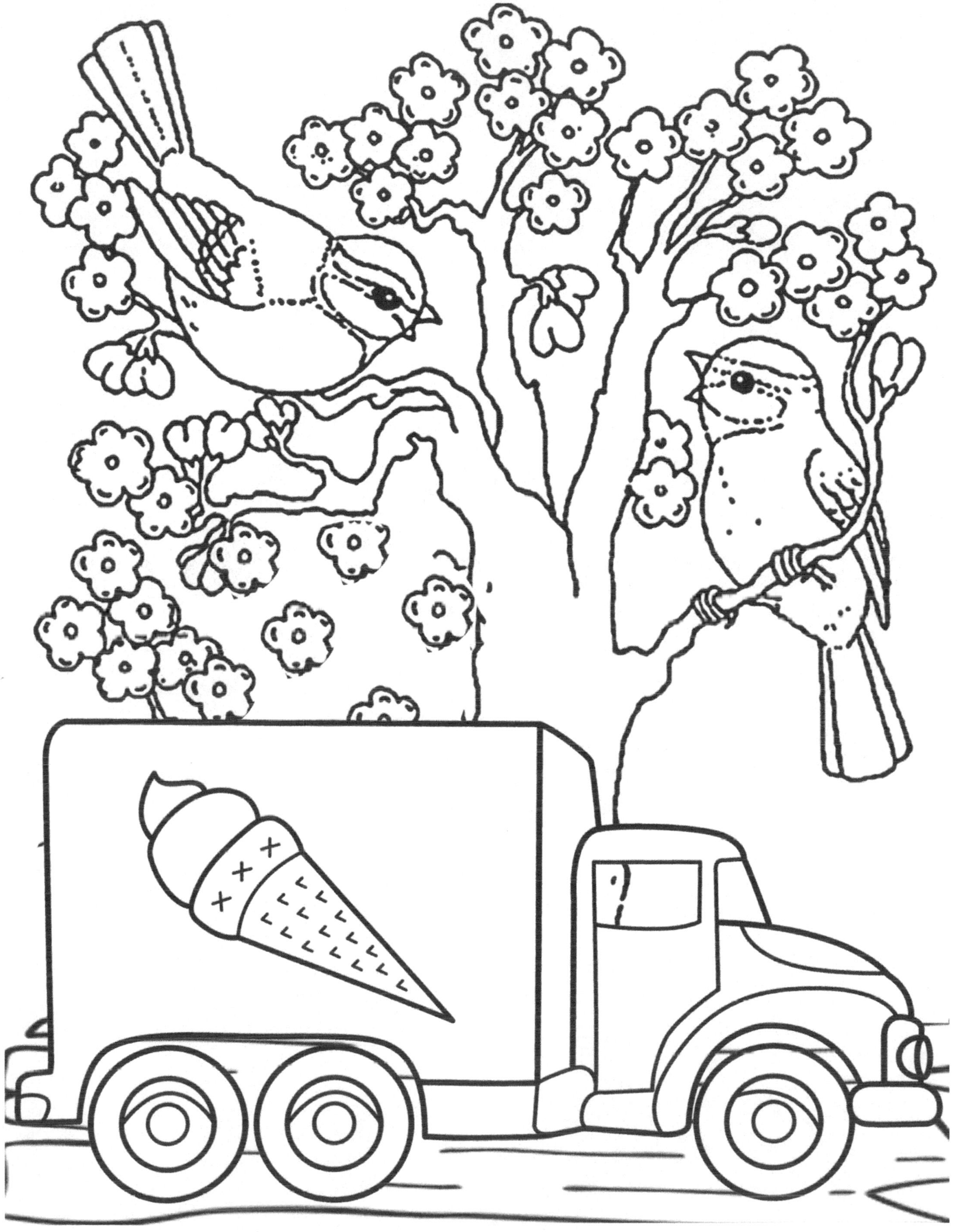

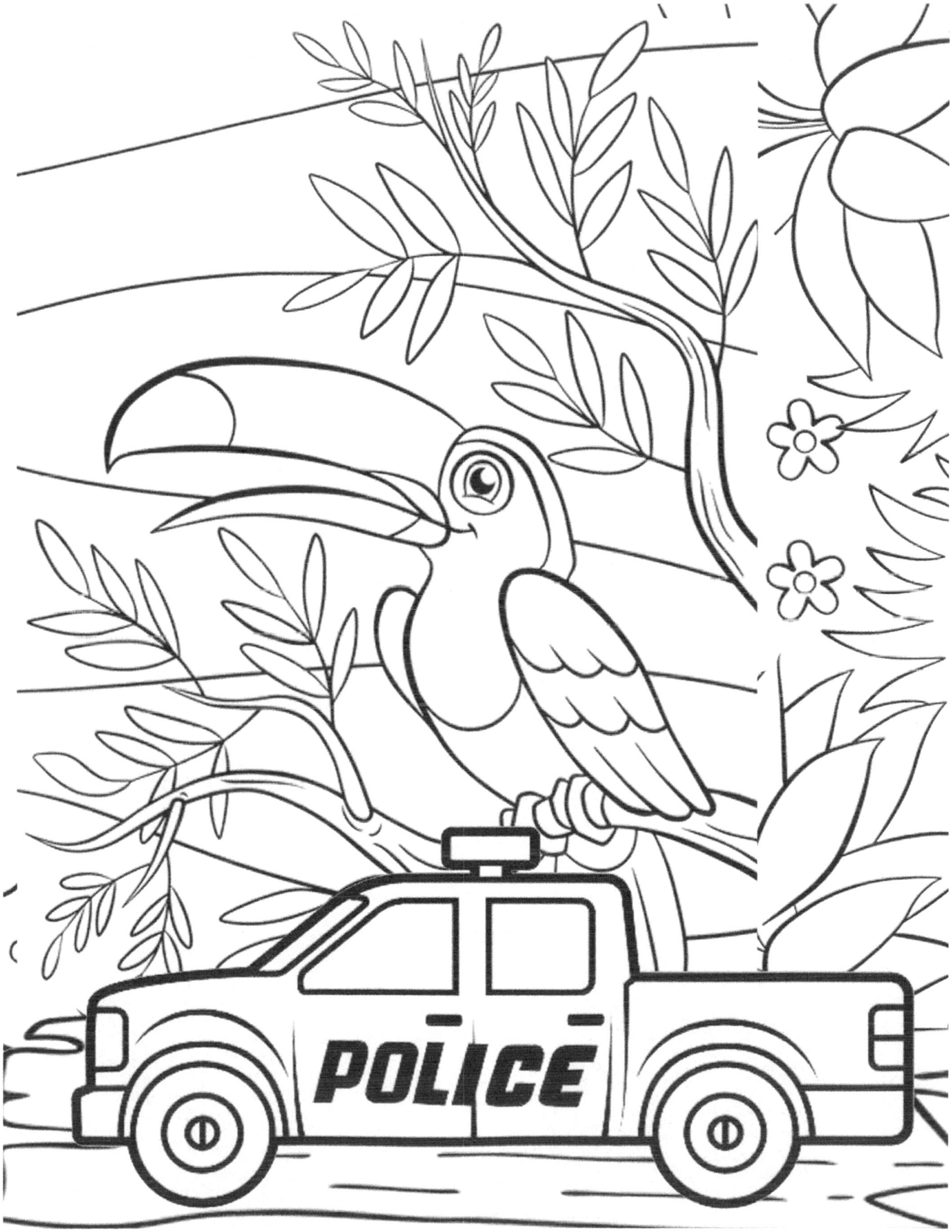
POLICE

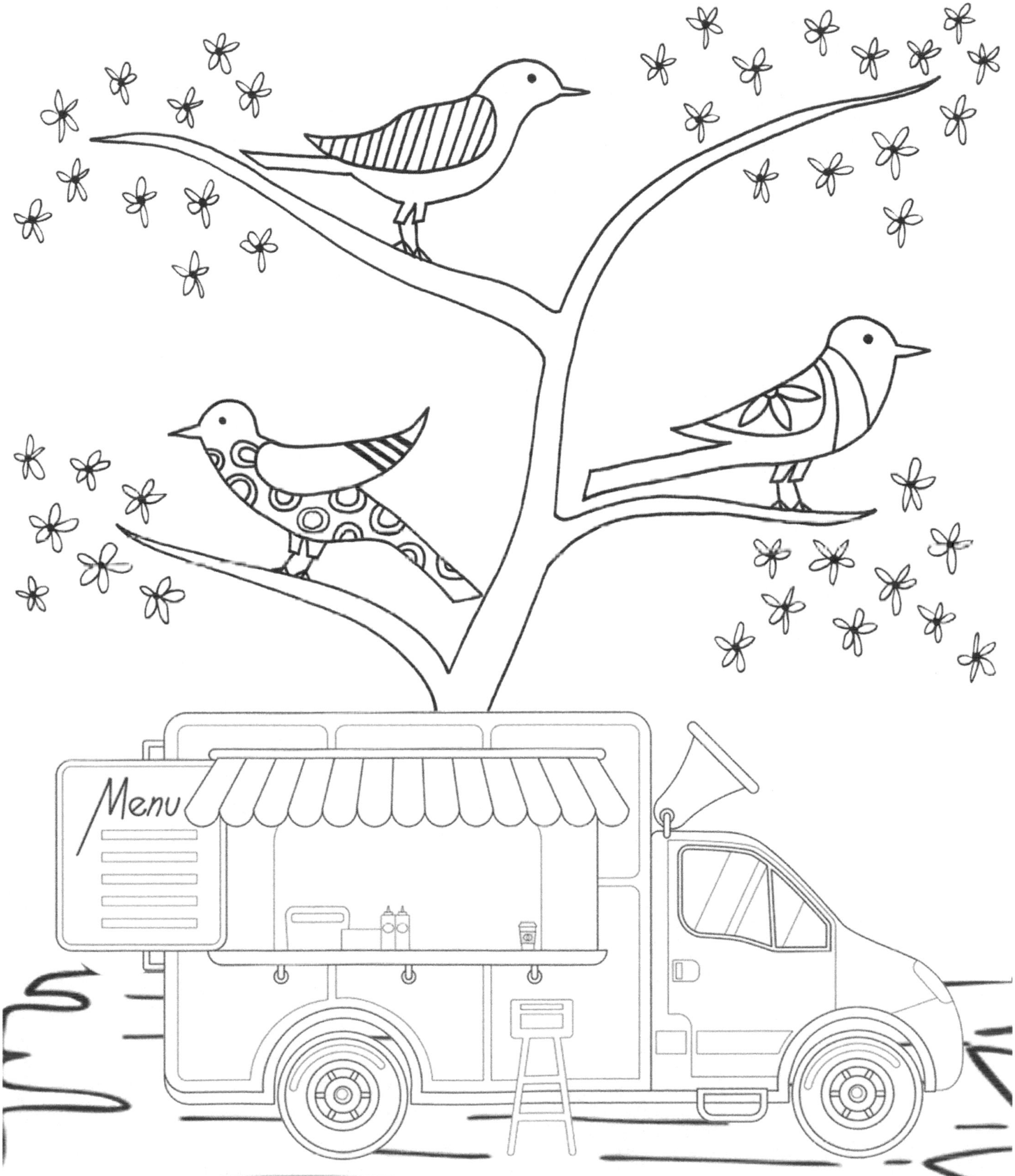

z

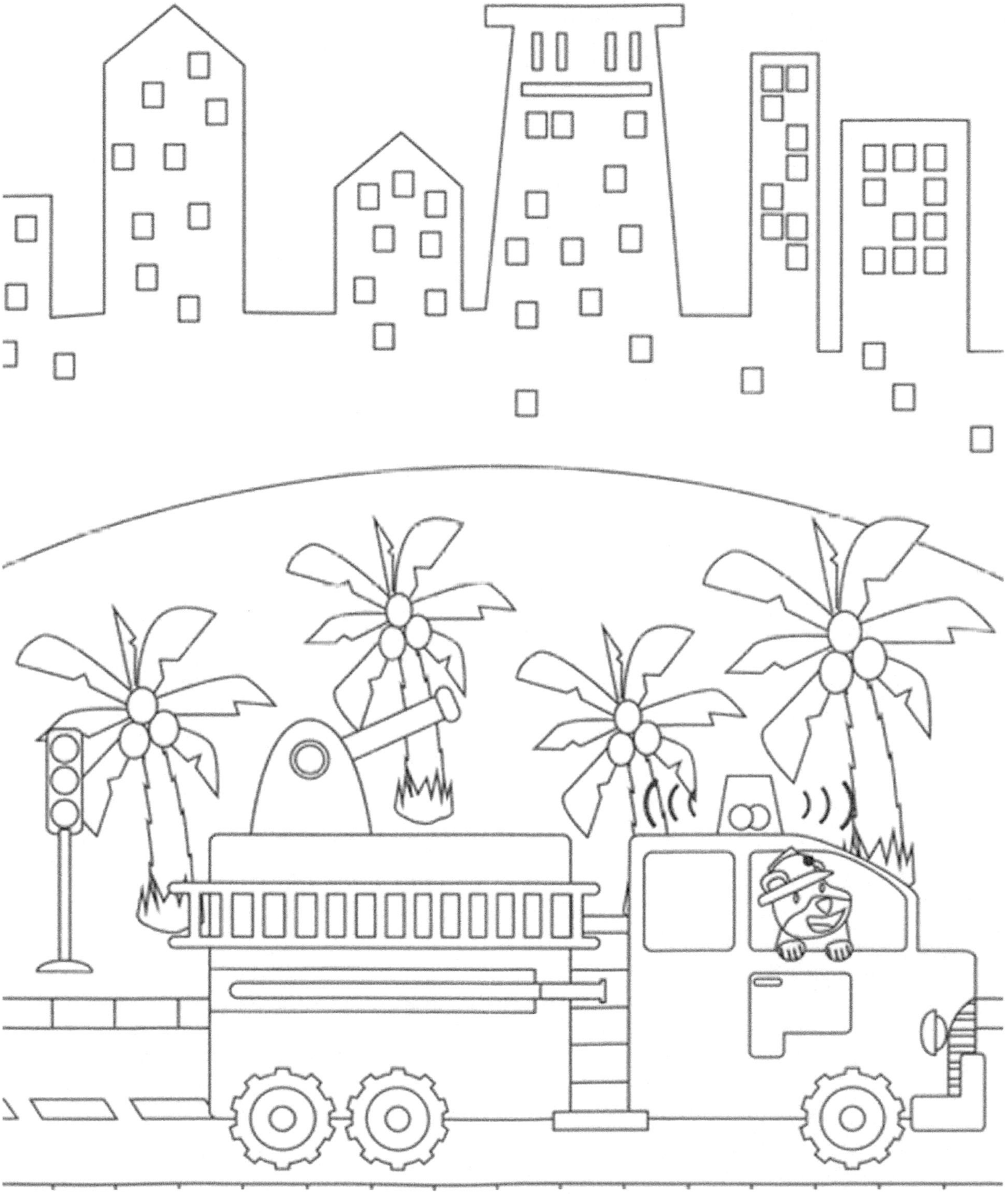

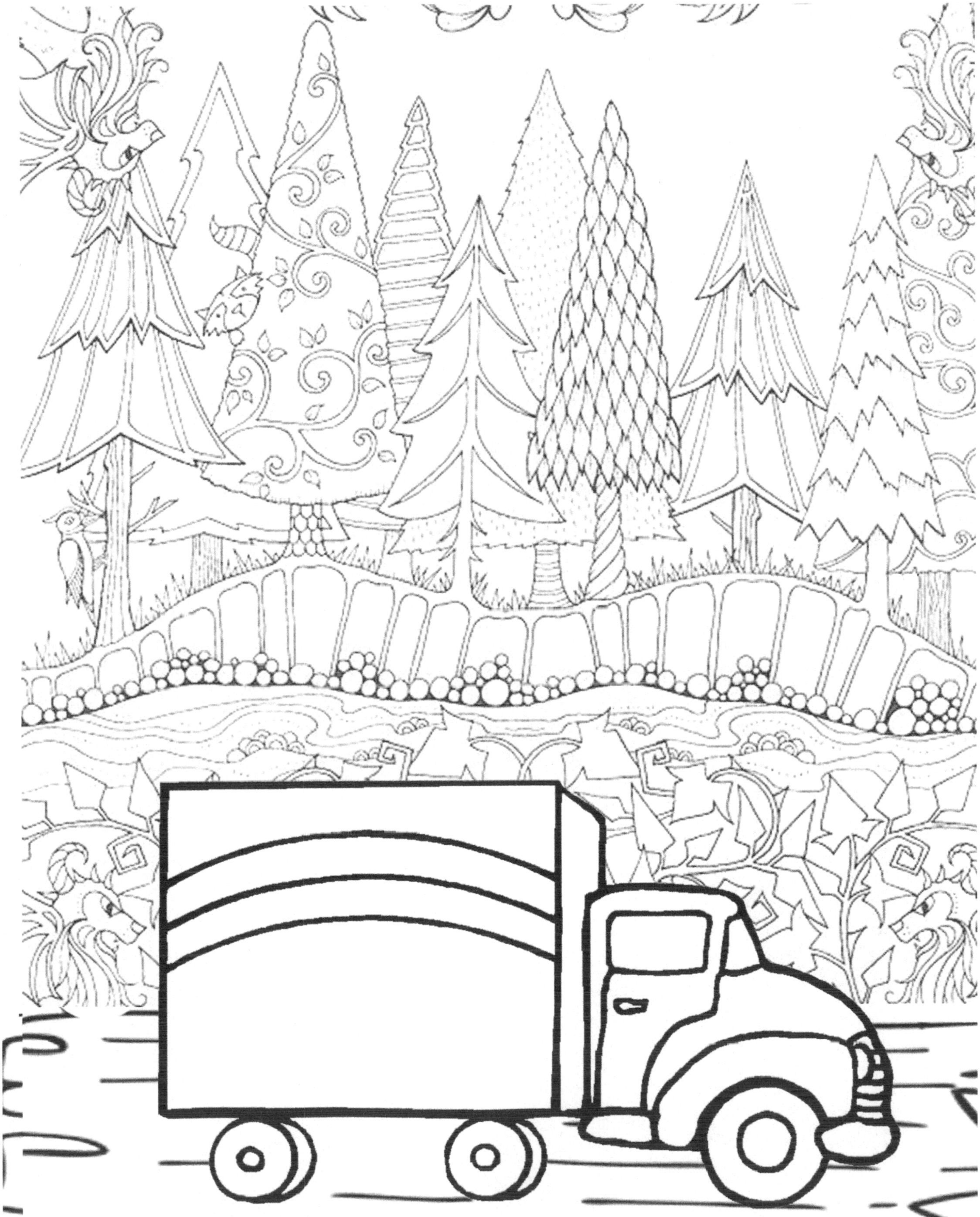

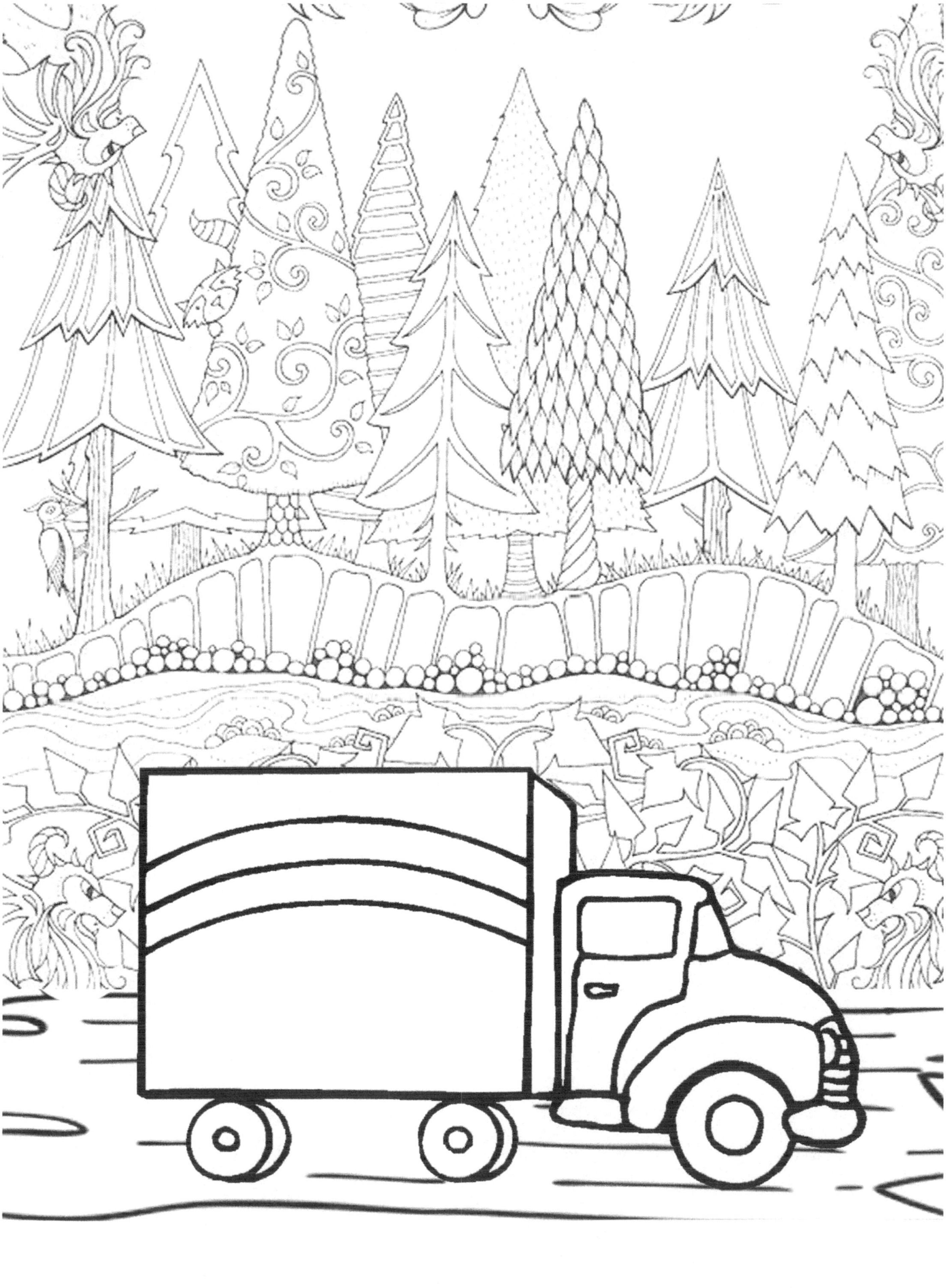

Made in the USA
Coppell, TX
15 January 2020

14527865R00026